THE REAL
MOTHER GOOSE

GOSLING
EDITION

RAND McNALLY & COMPANY
CHICAGO

THE REAL MOTHER GOOSE

LITTLE TOM TUCKER

Little Tom Tucker
　　Sings for his supper.
What shall he eat?
　　White bread and butter.

How will he cut it
　　Without e'er a knife?
How will he be married
　　Without e'er a wife?

JACK SPRAT

Jack Sprat
Could eat no fat,
His wife could eat no lean;
And so,
Betwixt them both,
They licked the platter clean.

THE PUMPKIN-EATER

Peter, Peter, pumpkin-eater,
Had a wife and couldn't keep her;
He put her in a pumpkin shell,
And there he kept her very well.

MARY, MARY, QUITE CONTRARY

Mary, Mary, quite contrary,
   How does your garden grow?
Silver bells and cockle-shells,
   And pretty maids all of a row.

IF

If all the world were apple pie,
   And all the sea were ink,
And all the trees were bread and
   cheese,
   What should we have for drink?

If wishes were horses, beggars would
ride.
If turnips were watches, I would
wear one by my side.

As I was going up Pippen Hill,
    Pippen Hill was dirty;
There I met a pretty Miss,
    And she dropped me a curtsy.

GOING TO ST. IVES

As I was going to St. Ives
I met a man with seven wives.
Every wife had seven sacks,
Every sack had seven cats,
Every cat had seven kits.
Kits, cats, sacks, and wives,
How many were going to St. Ives?

LADYBIRD

Ladybird, ladybird, fly away home!
Your house is on fire, your children
    all gone,
All but one, and her name is Ann,
And she crept under the pudding
    pan.

BANBURY CROSS

Ride a cock-horse to Banbury Cross,
To see an old lady upon a white
    horse.
Rings on her fingers, and bells on
    her toes,
She shall have music wherever she
    goes.

MISS MUFFET

Little Miss Muffet
    Sat on a tuffet,
Eating of curds and whey;
    There came a big spider,
    And sat down beside her,
And frightened Miss Muffet away.

SING A SONG OF SIXPENCE

Sing a song of sixpence,
    A pocket full of rye;
Four-and-twenty blackbirds
    Baked in a pie!

When the pie was opened
    The birds began to sing;
Was not that a dainty dish
    To set before the king?

The king was in his counting-house,
    Counting out his money;
The queen was in the parlor,
    Eating bread and honey.

The maid was in the garden,
    Hanging out the clothes;

When down came a blackbird
And snapped off her nose.

DAPPLE-GRAY

I had a little pony,
　　His name was Dapple-Gray;
I lent him to a lady,
　　To ride a mile away.
She whipped him, she slashed him,
　　She rode him through the mire;
I would not lend my pony now
　　For all the lady's hire.

THE TEN O'CLOCK
SCHOLAR

A diller, a dollar, a ten o'clock scholar!
　　What makes you come so soon?
You used to come at ten o'clock,
　　But now you come at noon.

ROBIN REDBREAST

Little Robin Redbreast sat upon a
    tree,
Up went Pussy Cat, down went he.
Down came Pussy Cat, away Robin
    ran,
Says little Robin Redbreast: "Catch
    me if you can!"

Little Robin Redbreast jumped upon
    a spade,
Pussy Cat jumped after him, and
    then he was afraid.
Little Robin chirped and sang, and
    what did Pussy say?
Pussy Cat said: "Mew, mew, mew,"
    and Robin flew away.

LITTLE JACK HORNER

Little Jack Horner
Sat in the corner,
Eating of Christmas pie:
He put in his thumb,
And pulled out a plum,
And said, "What a good boy am I!"

THE OLD WOMAN OF
LEEDS

There was an old woman of Leeds,
Who spent all her time in good
deeds;
She worked for the poor
Till her fingers were sore,
This pious old woman of Leeds!

NEEDLES AND PINS

Needles and pins, needles and pins,
When a man marries his trouble
   begins.

FOREHEAD, EYES, CHEEKS, NOSE, MOUTH, AND CHIN

Here sits the Lord Mayor,
   Here sit his two men,
Here sits the cock,
   Here sits the hen,
Here sit the little chickens,
   Here they run in.
Chin-chopper, chin-chopper, chin-
   chopper chin!

BAA, BAA, BLACK SHEEP

Baa, baa, black sheep,
    Have you any wool?
Yes, marry, have I,
    Three bags full;

One for my master,
    One for my dame,
But none for the little boy
    Who cries in the lane.

A B C

Great A, little a,
    Bouncing B!
The cat's in the cupboard,
    And can't see me.

I'll tell you a story

About Jack-a-Nory:

And now my story's begun.

I'll tell you another

About his brother:

And now my story is done.

Hickety, pickety,
My black hen,
She lays eggs for gentlemen;
Gentlemen come every day
To see what my black hen doth lay.

OLD WOMAN AND PEDDLER

There was an old woman, as I've heard
    tell,
She went to market her eggs for to sell;
She went to market all on a market day,
And she fell asleep on the King's
    highway.

There came by a peddler whose name
    was Stout,
He cut her petticoats all round about;
He cut her petticoats up to the knees,
Which made the old woman to shiver
    and freeze.

When the little old woman first did wake,
She began to shiver and she began to
    shake;

She began to wonder and she began to
     cry,
"Lauk a mercy on me, this can't be I!"

"But if it be I, as I hope it be,
I've a little dog at home, and he'll
     know me;
If it be I, he'll wag his little tail,
And if it be not I, he'll loudly bark and
     wail."

Home went the little woman all in the
     dark;
Up got the little dog, and he began to
     bark;
He began to bark, so she began to cry,
"Lauk a mercy on me, this is none of I!"

THERE WAS AN OLD WOMAN

There was an old woman who lived
in a shoe.

She had so many children she didn't
know what to do.

She gave them some broth without
any bread.

She whipped them all soundly and
put them to bed.

THE BOY IN THE BARN

A little boy went into a barn,
And lay down on some hay.
An owl came out, and flew about,
And the little boy ran away.

THE FARMER AND THE RAVEN

A farmer went trotting upon his
    gray mare,
    Bumpety, bumpety, bump!

With his daughter behind him so
    rosy and fair,
    Lumpety, lumpety, lump!

A raven cried croak! and they all
    tumbled down,
    Bumpety, bumpety, bump!

The mare broke her knees, and the
    farmer his crown,
    Lumpety, lumpety, lump!

The mischievous raven flew laugh-
    ing away,
  Bumpety, bumpety, bump!

And vowed he would serve them
    the same the next day,
  Lumpety, lumpety, lump!

BYE, BABY BUNTING

Bye, baby bunting,
Father's gone a-hunting,
Mother's gone a-milking,
Sister's gone a-silking,
And brother's gone to buy a skin
To wrap the baby bunting in.

BETTY BLUE

Little Betty Blue
Lost her holiday shoe;
What shall little Betty do?
Give her another
To match the other,
And then she'll walk upon two.

THE KING OF FRANCE

The King of France went up the
hill,
With twenty thousand men;
The King of France came down the
hill,
And ne'er went up again.

OLD MOTHER HUBBARD

Old Mother Hubbard
Went to the cupboard,
    To give her poor dog a bone;
But when she got there
The cupboard was bare,
    And so the poor dog had none.

She went to the baker's
    To buy him some bread;
When she came back
    The dog was dead.

She went to the undertaker's
    To buy him a coffin;
When she got back
    The dog was laughing.

.   .   .   .   .

She went to the cobbler's
    To buy him some shoes;
When she came back
    He was reading the news.

She went to the sempster's
    To buy him some linen;
When she came back
    The dog was a-spinning.

She went to the hosier's
    To buy him some hose;
When she came back
    He was dressed in his clothes.

The dame made a curtsy,
    The dog made a bow;
The dame said, "Your servant,"
    The dog said, "Bow-wow."

ROCK-A-BYE, BABY

Rock-a-bye, baby, thy cradle is green;
Father's a nobleman, mother's a
queen;
And Betty's a lady, and wears a
gold ring;
And Johnny's a drummer, and
drums for the king.

THE TARTS

The Queen of Hearts,
She made some tarts,
All on a summer's day;
The Knave of Hearts,
He stole the tarts,
And took them clean away.

The King of Hearts
Called for the tarts,
And beat the Knave full sore;
The Knave of Hearts
Brought back the tarts,
And vowed he'd steal no more.

TOM, TOM, THE PIPER'S SON

Tom, Tom, the piper's son,

Stole a pig, and away he run.

The pig was eat,

And Tom was beat,

And Tom ran crying down the street.

CROSS PATCH

Cross patch, draw the latch,

Sit by the fire and spin;

Take a cup and drink it up,

Then call your neighbors in.

LUCY LOCKET

Lucy Locket lost her pocket,
Kitty Fisher found it;
Nothing in it, nothing in it,
But the binding round it.

LITTLE BOY BLUE

Little Boy Blue, come, blow your
horn!
The sheep's in the meadow, the
cow's in the corn.
Where's the little boy that looks
after the sheep?
Under the haystack, fast asleep!

"To bed! To bed!"
Says Sleepy-head;
"Tarry awhile," says Slow;
"Put on the pan,"
Says Greedy Nan;
"We'll sup before we go."

Doctor Foster went to Glo'ster,
  In a shower of rain;
He stepped in a puddle, up to his middle,
  And never went there again.

THE CAT AND THE FIDDLE

Hey, diddle, diddle!
The cat and the fiddle,
The cow jumped over the moon;
The little dog laughed
To see such sport,
And the dish ran away with the
spoon.

BURNIE BEE

Burnie bee, burnie bee,
Tell me when your wedding be?
If it be tomorrow day,
Take your wings and fly away.

TOMMY SNOOKS

As Tommy Snooks and Bessy Brooks
    Were walking out one Sunday,
Says Tommy Snooks to Bessy Brooks,
    "Wilt marry me on Monday?"

A STRANGE OLD WOMAN

There was an old woman, and what
    do you think?
She lived upon nothing but victuals
    and drink;
Victuals and drink were the chief
    of her diet,
And yet this old woman could
    never be quiet.

AS I WAS GOING ALONG

As I was going along, along,
A-singing a comical song, song, song,
The lane that I went was so long,
    long, long,
And the song that I sang was so
    long, long, long,
And so I went singing along.

THREE WISE MEN OF
GOTHAM

Three wise men of Gotham
Went to sea in a bowl;
If the bowl had been stronger,
My song had been longer.

BOBBY SHAFTOE

Bobby Shaftoe's gone to sea,
With silver buckles on his knee;
He'll come back and marry me,
    Pretty Bobby Shaftoe!
Bobby Shaftoe's fat and fair,
Combing down his yellow hair;
He's my love for evermore.
    Pretty Bobby Shaftoe.

LITTLE JUMPING JOAN

Here am I, little jumping Joan,
When nobody's with me
    I'm always alone.

TONGS

Long legs, crooked thighs,
Little head, and no eyes.

THE CROOKED
SIXPENCE

There was a crooked man, and he
went a crooked mile,
He found a crooked sixpence be-
side a crooked stile;
He bought a crooked cat, which
caught a crooked mouse,
And they all lived together in a
little crooked house.

A CANDLE

Little Nanny Etticoat
In a white petticoat,
    And a red nose;
The longer she stands
    The shorter she grows.

THE ROBIN

The north wind doth blow,
And we shall have snow,
And what will poor robin do then,
                Poor thing?
He'll sit in a barn,
And keep himself warm,
And hide his head under his wing,
                Poor thing!

ONE, TWO, BUCKLE MY SHOE

One, two,
Buckle my shoe;
Three, four,
Knock at the door;
Five, six,
Pick up sticks;
Seven, eight,
Lay them straight;
Nine, ten,
A good, fat hen;
Eleven, twelve,
Dig and delve;
Thirteen, fourteen,
Maids a-courting;

Fifteen, sixteen,
Maids in the kitchen;
Seventeen, eighteen;
Maids a-waiting;
Nineteen, twenty,
My plate's empty.

PEASE PORRIDGE

Pease porridge hot,
    Pease porridge cold,
Pease porridge in the pot,
    Nine days old.
Some like it hot,
    Some like it cold,
Some like it in the pot,
    Nine days old.

HARK! HARK!

Hark, hark! the dogs do bark!
    Beggars are coming to town:
Some in jags, and some in rags,
    And some in velvet gown.

ONE MISTY MOISTY MORNING

One misty moisty morning,
    When cloudy was the weather,
I chanced to meet an old man,
    Clothed all in leather.
He began to compliment
    And I began to grin.
How do you do? And how do you do?
    And how do you do again?

HUMPTY DUMPTY

Humpty Dumpty sat on a wall,
Humpty Dumpty had a great fall;
All the King's horses, and all the
King's men
Cannot put Humpty Dumpty to-
gether again.

THE MOUSE AND THE CLOCK

Hickory, dickory, dock!
The mouse ran up the clock;
The clock struck one,
And down he run,
Hickory, dickory, dock!

BARBER

Barber, barber, shave a pig.
How many hairs will make a wig?
Four and twenty; that's enough.
Give the barber a pinch of snuff.

DIDDLE DIDDLE
DUMPLING

Diddle diddle dumpling, my son
    John
Went to bed with his breeches on,
One stocking off, and one stocking
    on;
Diddle diddle dumpling, my son
    John.

There was an old woman
Lived under a hill;
And if she's not gone,
She lives there still.

See a pin and pick it up,
All the day you'll have good luck.
See a pin and let it lay,
Bad luck you'll have all the day.

JUST LIKE ME

"I went up one pair of stairs."
"Just like me."

"I went up two pairs of stairs."
"Just like me."

"I went into a room."
"Just like me."

"I looked out of a window."
"Just like me."

"And there I saw a monkey."
"Just like me."

PETER PIPER

Peter Piper picked a peck of
  pickled peppers;
A peck of pickled peppers Peter
  Piper picked.
If Peter Piper picked a peck of
  pickled peppers,
Where's the peck of pickled peppers
  Peter Piper picked?

CAESAR'S SONG

  Bow-wow-wow!
Whose dog art thou?
Little Tom Tinker's dog,
  Bow-wow-wow!

A LITTLE MAN

There was a little man,
And he had a little gun,
And his bullets were made of
lead, lead, lead;
He went to the brook,
And saw a little duck,
And shot it right through the
head, head, head.

He carried it home
To his old wife Joan,
And bade her a fire to make,
make, make,
To roast the little duck
He had shot in the brook,

And he'd go and fetch the drake,
drake, drake.

TO MARKET

To market, to market, to buy a fat
    pig,
Home again, home again, jiggety jig.
To market, to market, to buy a fat
    hog,
Home again, home again, jiggety
    jog.
To market, to market, to buy a plum
    bun,
Home again, home again, market is
    done.

RAIN

Rain, rain, go to Spain,
And never come back again.

GOOD ADVICE

Come when you're called,
    Do what you're bid,
Shut the door after you,
    And never be chid.

POOR OLD ROBINSON CRUSOE!

Poor old Robinson Crusoe!
Poor old Robinson Crusoe!
    They made him a coat
    Of an old Nanny goat.
I wonder why they should do so!
    With a ring-a-ting-tang,
    And a ring-a-ting-tang,
Poor old Robinson Crusoe!

COCK-A-DOODLE-DO!

Cock-a-doodle-do!
My dame has lost her shoe,
My master's lost his fiddle-stick,
And knows not what to do.

Cock-a-doodle-do!
What is my dame to do?
Till master finds his fiddle-stick,
She'll dance without her shoe.

DAFFODILS

Daffy-down-dilly has come to town
In a yellow petticoat and a green
gown.

CURLY-LOCKS

Curly-locks, Curly-locks, wilt thou
    be mine?
Thou shalt not wash the dishes,
    nor yet feed the swine;
But sit on a cushion, and sew a
    fine seam,
And feed upon strawberries, sugar,
    and cream.

FOR EVERY EVIL

For every evil under the sun
There is a remedy or there is
    none.
If there be one, seek till you find
    it;
If there be none, never mind it.

A NEEDLE AND THREAD

Old Mother Twichett had but one
eye,
And a long tail which she let fly;
And every time she went through
a gap,
A bit of her tail she left in a trap.

THREE BLIND MICE

Three blind mice!
See how they run!
They all ran after the farmer's wife,
Who cut off their tails with a carv-
ing knife.
Did you ever see such a thing in
your life
As three blind mice?

PAT-A-CAKE

Pat-a-cake, pat-a-cake,
    Baker's man!
So I do, master,
    As fast as I can.

Pat it, and prick it,
    And mark it with T,
Put it in the oven
    For Tommy and me.